TO **B**IRD
OR NOT TO **B**IRD

Archimedes' Printing Shoppe
& Sundry Goodes

TO BIRD
OR NOT TO BIRD

S.J. RUSSELL & LUCY NOLAND
ILLUSTRATED BY KAITY LACY

Printed on tree-free bamboo paper stock with soy-based, eco-friendly inks in China. Cover and spine in 100% recycled Eska® board.

Design by A Little Graphix
Chinchilla, Grandma, Athelas

Enormous gratitude to ecologist Melissa McCormick, naturalist Ray A. Mendez, and Michael J. Parr, President of the American Bird Conservancy, for their expert help with the "Fabulous Facts" of *To Bird or Not to Bird*.

Library of Congress Cataloging-in-Publication Data
LCCN: 2022942736 | ISBN: : 978-1-955517-05-8
Classification: LCC PZ7.1.N6375 Tob 2023 | DDC [E]--dc23
Names: Russell, S.J., author. | Noland, Lucy, author. | Lacy, Kaity, illustrator.
Title: To bird or not to bird
S.J. Russell and Lucy Noland; illustrated by Kaity Lacy.

Summary: *To Bird or Not to Bird* captures the wonderful moment a bird and a worm meet, take the time to get to know one another, and ponder how different things would be if they couldn't do the wonderful things they do.

Subjects: Birds–Juvenile fiction| Nature–Juvenile fiction | JNF003000–Juvenile nonfiction | Animals / General | Science & Nature / General

For our Bobs

who have made our world
a magical place.

TO BIRD
OR NOT TO BIRD

Bustling Bird

soared

in the sky.

Wiggling Worm wriggled low.

Working Worm hummed soft tunes.

Bubbly Bird warbled bold ones.

Bird spied Worm.
And Worm sensed Bird.

"You're
different than
me,"

were the words
each heard.

"Worm,
why dig so deep?"
babbled Bird.

Said **Worm** to **Bird**,

"Why fly so **high?**"

"I'm birding

and have **babies** to feed," said **Bird**.

"I help grasses,
bushes and trees by widely *sowing*
their seeds.
Can't **you** fly like **me**?"

"No, you see," murmured Worm,
"I'm worming,
which means I'm burrowing and
eating up earth's fallen things,
what many call 'recycling.'"

Bird scratched his head with his thinking **wing**, "But what if **you** were not to **worm**?"

Worm curled into a little ball,
"I think there'd be a problem then
if I could not poop nutrients.
Who would build these many holes
to aerate soil and help things grow?
How upset would gardeners be
if it weren't for worms like me?"

Worm filled with curiosity,

"And what if **you** were not to **bird**?"

Bird laughed out loud at such a thought

and then his eyes grew wide,

"Sure, who would serenade the skies?

Or gobble down a thousand flies?

How itchy would the people be?

Who else's poop could plant a tree

if not for me?"

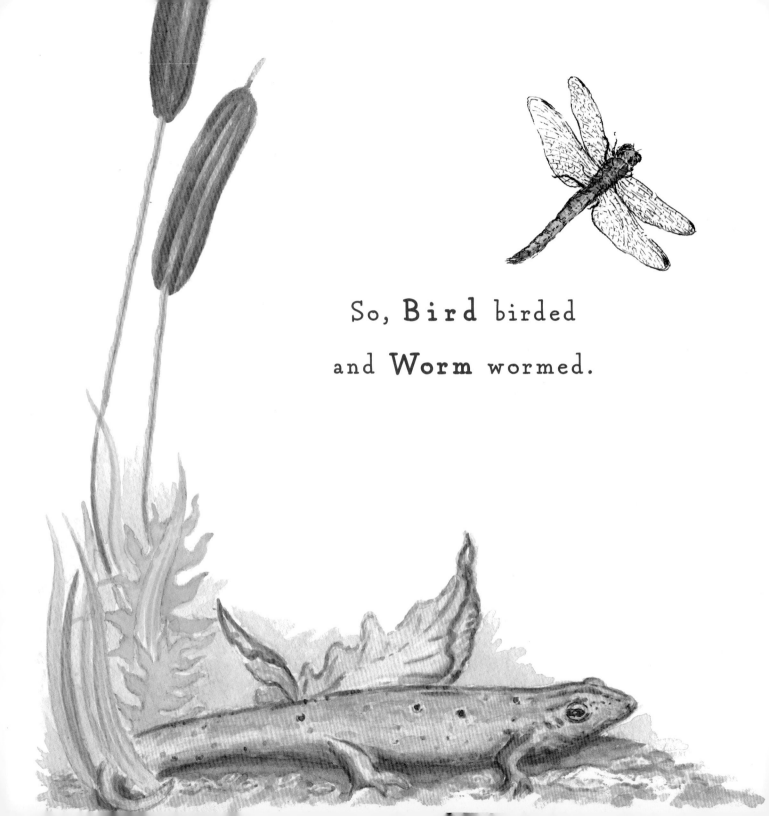

So, **Bird** birded
and **Worm** wormed.

And both were **amazed**

at what they'd **learned**.

FABULOUS FACTS
ABOUT RED-WINGED BLACKBIRDS
AND EARTHWORMS

Birds and worms—like humans—are animals.
*The **animal kingdom** has two main **groups**:*

vertebrates—those with backbones like **humans** and **birds**
invertebrates—those without backbones like **worms**

MEET
BIRD!

Lifespan:
on average, two and a half years in the wild,
but wait until you read about the oldest wild
red-winged blackbird discovered so far!

Red-winged blackbirds

sing their songs all across North America, from Alaska through Canada and as far south as Central America and The Bahamas. Since they don't have winter coats to keep warm during cold months, birds that live in the north during the spring and summer fly south when autumn arrives. That's called "migrating"—moving from one area to another area depending on the seasons.

Red-winged blackbird migrations are amazing! Their flocks can look like an endless river of flapping wings overhead with as many as a million birds flying together. Red-winged blackbirds will travel with other birds like grackles, cowbirds, starlings, and even robins. Males migrate with males and females with females. Some red-winged blackbirds fly as far as 750 miles to get to their seasonal home. They only fly during the day, because just like you, they have to get a good night's sleep. It can take weeks for them to finally arrive at their destination.

Male and female red-winged blackbirds look entirely different. The boys are glossy black with bright reddish-orange and yellow shoulder patches. The girls are mostly dark brown with a streaked pattern and light-colored eyebrows. Their coloring helps them blend with the surroundings, staying hidden while with their eggs or babies.

Do you love splashing in water? If you answered "Yes!" you're like a red-winged blackbird! They love raising their families around water. A mom-to-be weaves a little basket out of stringy plants, wet leaves, and old wood. She packs the inside with mud, then lines it with soft grasses to make a cozy nest for her chicks. So much work! Sometimes you'll spot her nest in bushes or up in trees, but often red-winged blackbirds will build their nests around tall grassy plants like cattails that grow in wetlands. Those above-water nests protect babies from predators that do not like splashing in water.

Red-winged blackbirds are fiercely protective of their nests. Get too close and they'll divebomb whether you're a much bigger bird or a person. It's all about keeping their babies safe. And fed. Babies eat a lot.

Good thing both moms and dads feed their babies! They take turns bringing food every 10 to 20 minutes from dawn to dusk.

In the spring and summer months, insects are the star of their menu. Red-winged blackbirds help keep insect populations balanced so ecosystems can thrive (and you don't get as many bites from mosquitos and flies). In the fall and winter, they eat mostly seeds, but fruits and grains end up in their bellies as well. Birds that gobble up seeds and fruits help new plants grow. How? Their poop! It contains seeds that can sprout into new plants all across the places they fly. In fact, some plants like blackberries and raspberries need to pass through an animal's digestive tract to be able to sprout.

Guess what red-winged blackbirds and other birds sprouted from, so to speak. Dinosaurs! Birds are actually teeny-tiny dinosaurs descended specifically from the three-toed kind that includes the towering *Tyrannosaurus rex* and the much smaller *Velociraptor*. And just like birds, *Velociraptors* were covered in fluffy feathers. Yep! They didn't look like lizards at all!

Speaking of old, the oldest red-winged blackbird ever discovered was 15 years and nine months old. How do scientists know this? Well, a researcher in New Jersey put a band on one of the bird's legs in 1967. Almost 16 years later, someone in Michigan found the bird injured, helped him recover then released him back into the wild.

MEET WORM!

Lifespan:
from one to 10 years depending on the earthworm.

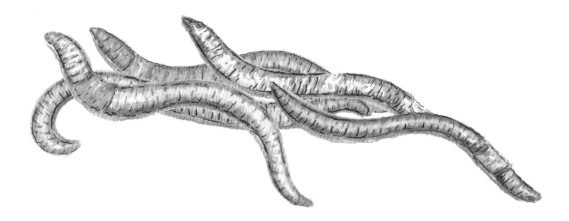

Earthworms

Earthworms live on every continent in the world except for Antarctica, because it's just too *c-c-c-cold!* They've been tunneling through the soil and munching on decaying leaves since dinosaurs roamed. Scientists think the ancestor of all earthworms lived more than 200 million years ago. Today, more than 7,000 kinds of earthworms are wriggling all around us. One acre of land can be home to more than one million earthworms—that's a whole lot of wriggling!

Most earthworms live in the soil—some deep down and others near the surface. Many love life in fallen leaves (called leaf litter). Others make their homes in decaying logs, riverbanks, and along the seashore. Some earthworms even live in trees!

Worms are like rainbows. Worms are like what?? Earthworms come in all colors of the rainbow. The ones that live mostly deep in the soil tend to be whitish or even a bit purple. Some are green; others are aquamarine blue. Of course, you probably know about pink, red and reddish-brown earthworms. But did you know that some are deep indigo blue with wonderfully bright yellow spots? Or, that others even glow? Yep! They're what's called "bioluminescent," which means they create their own light.

Though earthworms come in one shape—a tube—they come in all sizes, from less than a half inch to ginormous! In 1967, the longest earthworm ever discovered wiggled to fame in South Africa. That worm was almost 22 feet long. Imagine four park

benches lined up next to each other and then add another foot!

Body parts: *You* have one fabulous heart and two lungs. Earthworms have no lungs and **five** hearts (though their hearts are very simple compared to ours). How do earthworms breathe without lungs? They absorb oxygen *through* their skin, which needs to stay wet for them to breathe. But note: Too much water is very bad since earthworms can drown.

Eyes? Nope. Earthworms don't have eyes, but they do have special cells at the front of their body that sense light. Ears? That's another nope. But they "hear" by sensing vibrations through the ground. Mouth? Of course! That's how they can eat their weight in soil and 1/10 their weight in leaves every single day (leaves, of course, weigh a lot less than soil or earthworms). Hair? Before you say, "No way!" **Way!** Earthworms have itty-bitty stiff hairs on almost every segment of their body. These little hairs help earthworms move, and even accomplish incredible feats like climbing rain forest trees that are as tall as a 13-story building! When a baby earthworm is a few weeks old, you'll see a light-colored, swollen band forming near its head.

That band is called a "clitellum" (pronounced: kleye-TELL-um). Earthworms are both female and male and the clitellum helps to form a cocoon where babies grow until they hatch.

Psst! Here's a little-known secret: Most earthworms in Canada and the northern United States, like nightcrawlers, are not supposed to be here. The glaciers of the Ice Age wiped out earthworms. Early settlers from Europe brought their own earthworms, thinking they would help their gardens. Other earthworms accidentally hitched a ride in the soil used to weigh down ships. To this day, non-native species arrive in the roots of plants shipped from overseas. The problem: Forests in the north evolved with zero earthworms, and these areas now grow best without them.

However, native earthworms in their native habitats are eco-heroes! More than 100 species of native earthworms live south of the northernmost region in the United States and throughout the American West into Canada's British Columbia. These earthworms turn over, aerate, and drain soil. And, as you now know, they eat that soil, which is not only loaded with decaying vegetation but also tiny organisms like bacteria and fungi. Earthworm poop is packed with loads of nutrients that help plants grow. All that adds up to a gardener's and farmer's best friend! Hooray for native earthworms!

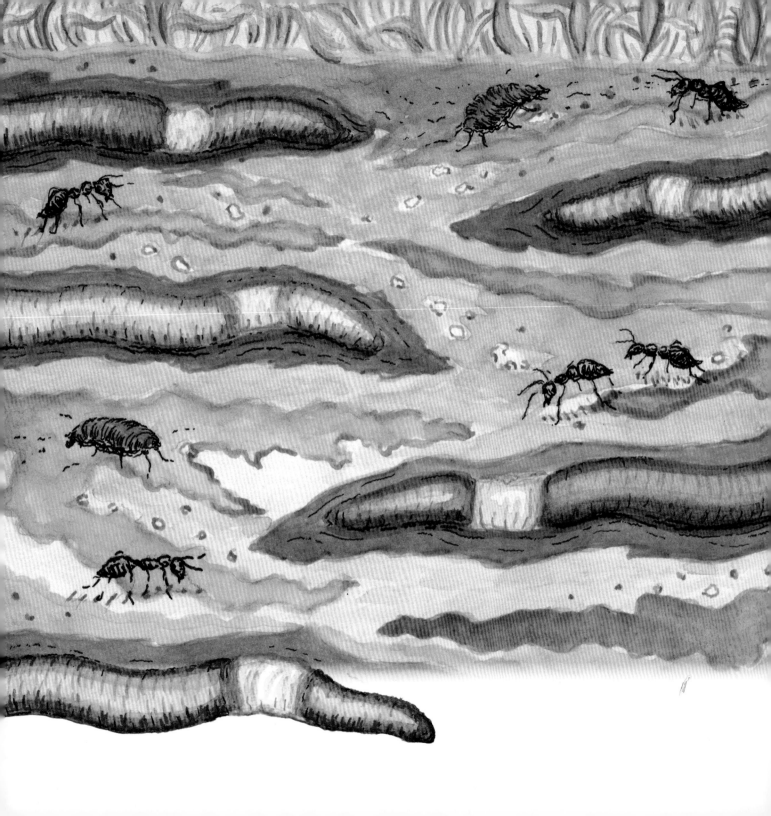

BONUS FACT

Worm, in our story, is a member of the species

Eisenoides lonnbergi
(pronounced: ay-seh-NOY-dehs lawn-BER-jee).

This native North American earthworm loves wetlands,
munching on decaying vegetation, and burrowing.

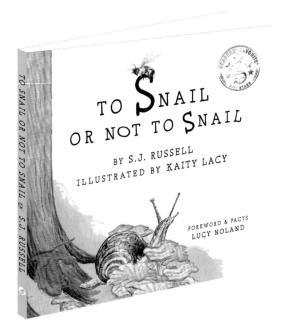

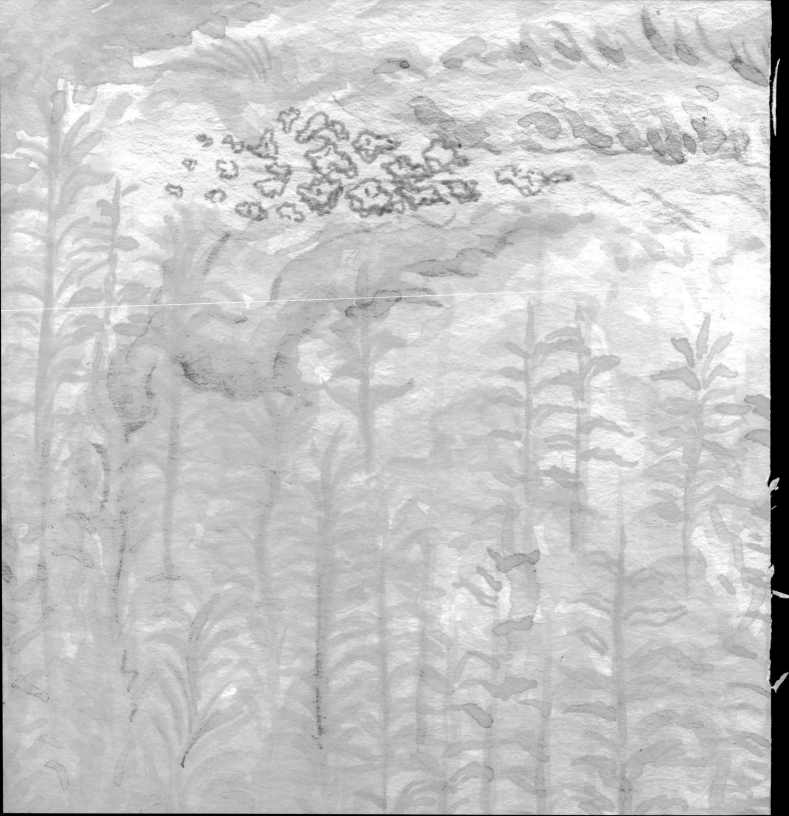